Garfield

Life and Lasagne

JIM DAVIS

Ravette London

This edition first published by
Ravette Limited 1986
Reprinted 1987 (twice), 1987

Printed and bound in Great Britain
for Ravette Limited,
3 Glenside Estate, Star Road, Partridge Green,
Horsham, Sussex RH13 8RA
by Cox & Wyman Ltd, Reading

ISBN 0 948456 11 6

© 1985 United Feature Syndicate, Inc.

© 1985 United Feature Syndicate, Inc.

© 1985 United Feature Syndicate, Inc.

© 1985 United Feature Syndicate, Inc.

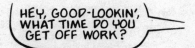

© 1985 United Feature Syndicate, Inc

© 1985 United Feature Syndicate, Inc.

10·22

NOW I WONDER WHAT NERMAL COULD BE UP TO

THERE'S A SHARK IN MY WATER BOWL!

OH

© 1985 United Feature Syndicate, Inc.

© 1985 United Feature Syndicate, Inc.

© 1985 United Feature Syndicate, Inc.

© 1985 United Feature Syndicate, Inc.

© 1985 United Feature Syndicate, Inc

WHATEVER JON PAID FOR THIS TV REMOTE CONTROL, IT WAS WORTH IT!

GARFIELD, THE VET SAYS YOU ARE GOING TO HAVE TO STAY INSIDE. THERE'S A RARE STRAIN OF HAWAIIAN CAT FLU GOING AROUND

3-19

TOO LATE, DOC

© 1985 United Feature Syndicate, Inc.

© 1985 United Feature Syndicate, Inc.

© 1985 United Feature Syndicate, Inc.

© 1985 United Feature Syndicate, Inc.

5-8

KISS

PETS ALWAYS SENSE WHEN YOU'RE GOING TO THE GROCERY

BUY ME A STEAK

© 1985 United Feature Syndicate, Inc.

© 1985 United Feature Syndicate, Inc.

© 1985 United Feature Syndicate, Inc.

© 1985 United Feature Syndicate, Inc.

© 1985 United Feature Syndicate, Inc

ZIP

© 1985 United Feature Syndicate, Inc.

9-12

JIM DAVIS

WHERE ARE YOU GOING?
THE MOVIE ISN'T OVER YET

THE MOVIE IS OVER
WHEN THE POPCORN
IS FINISHED

OTHER GARFIELD BOOKS IN THIS SERIES

LANDSCAPE SERIES

TV SPECIALS

Here Comes Garfield	£2.95
Garfield On The Town	£2.95
Garfield In The Rough	£2.95
Garfield In Disguise	£2.95
Garfield In Paradise	£2.95

All these books are available at your local bookshop or newsagent, or can be ordered direct from the publisher. Just tick the titles you require and fill in the form below. Prices and availability subject to change without notice.

Ravette Limited, 3 Glenside Estate, Star Road, Partridge Green, Horsham, West Sussex RH13 8RA

Please send a cheque or postal order, and allow the following for postage and packing. UK: Pocket-books and TV Specials — 45p for one book plus 20p for the second book and 15p for each additional book. Landscape Series — 45p for one book plus 30p for each additional book.

Name ....

Address ....

....